Spelling & Phonics Age 5-6

Shareen Mayers

In a strange place, not too far from here, lives a scare of monsters.

A 'scare' is what some people call a group of monsters, but these monsters are really very friendly once you get to know them.

They are a curious bunch – they look very unusual, but they are quite like you and me, and they love learning new things and having fun.

In this book you will go on a learning journey with the monsters and you are sure to have lots of fun along the way.

Do not forget to visit our website to find out more about all the monsters and to send us photos of you in your monster mask or the monsters that you draw and make!

Contents

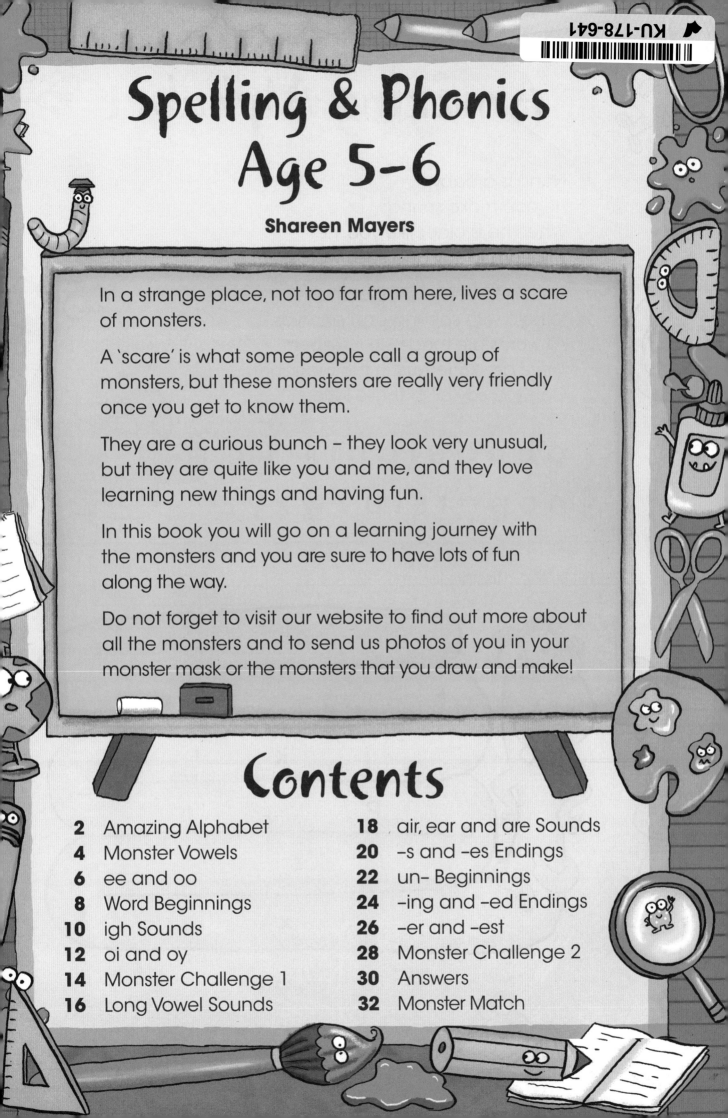

Amazing Alphabet

Nano is a baby.
He can make sounds.
When he is older, like you, he
will learn to say and spell words.

You need to know the alphabet
to help with spelling and phonics.
All words are made up of **letters**.
There are **26 letters** in the alphabet.
Can you say all of these letters?

a b c d e f g h i j k l m

n o p q r s t u v w x y z

1 Fill in the missing letters.

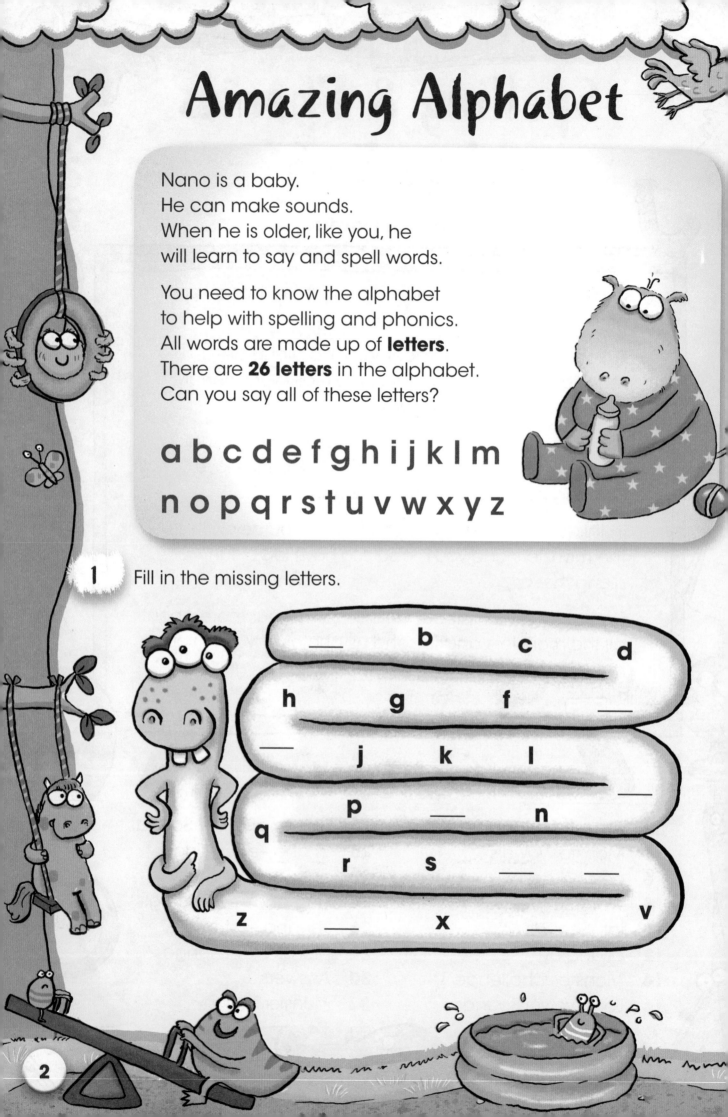

___	b	c	d
h	g	f	___
___	j	k	l
q	p	___	n
	r	s	___
z	___	x	v

2 Join up the letters in alphabetical order to find the monster pet.

Fun Zone!

Find all of the words in this word search.

Congratulations! You can now find and colour **Shape 1** on the Monster Match page!

j	u	m	p	s	e	r	o
l	v	y	v	q	f	v	v
a	i	y	g	u	o	q	e
z	z	i	p	i	x	s	r
y	o	o	m	c	r	t	o
t	d	o	g	k	d	s	u
h	b	b	r	o	w	n	c
e	w	y	u	u	f	r	p

the
quick
brown
fox
jumps
over
lazy
dog

Monster Vowels

Poggo is in the kitchen with Nano.
He is teaching Nano the names of objects
like pan, peg, bin, pot and cup.

There are **five vowels** in the alphabet:

a e i o u

Most words have at least one vowel.
The other letters are called **consonants**.

Make sure you choose the correct short
vowel sound when writing words.

b**a**g   b**u**g   b**i**g

---

1 Choose the correct vowel for each word.
The first one has been done for you.

a [a]   [e]
h_**a**_t

d [u]   [a]
t___b

g [e]   [i]
d____g

b [o]   [u]
r___d

e [a]   [e]
p___n

h [a]   [e]
p___n

c [i]   [e]
p___g

f [i]   [a]
w___g

i [u]   [o]
m___d

2 Draw a line to join the pairs of words that have the same vowel in the middle.

jam   leg   dot

log   zip   pup

bed   bib   cub   fan

3 Look at the words in **2**.
Write the correct word under each picture.

a   zip

c

e

g

i

b

d

f

h

j

Fun Zone!

Find five differences between these two pictures of Nano.

Well done! You can now find and colour **Shape 2** on the Monster Match page!

ee and oo

Mum likes to take Nano for walks.
They look for birds in the sky.
They spot cows in the fields.
Birds and cows make loud sounds!

Time to learn about the sounds **ee**
and **oo**.
They can be difficult to remember.
To help, you can think of birds and cows!

t+w+**ee**+t = tw**ee**t

m+**oo** = m**oo**

1 Add the **ee** sound to each of the words.
Write the whole words you make below.
The first one has been done for you.

a p_ee_l   **b** s_____   **c** tr_____   **d** gr____n   **e** m____t

peel

2 Add the **oo** sound to each of the words.
Write the whole words you make below.
The first one has been done for you.

a p_oo_l   **b** f____d   **c** m____n   **d** s____n   **e** z____

pool

3 Draw a line to join the pairs of words that rhyme.
Write the words next to the second word of each rhyme.
The first one has been done for you.

a seed   deep   _____   _____

b hoop   zoom   _____   _____

c keep   weed   <u>seed</u>   <u>weed</u>

d hoof   peek   _____   _____

e week   loop   _____   _____

f room   roof   _____   _____

4 Choose **ee** or **oo** to complete each word.

a | w_ee_k | **c** | fr_____ | **e** | r_____t | **g** | n___n | **i** | n____d |

b | tr_____p | **d** | w___p | **f** | gr____n | **h** | m____d | **j** | h____l |

Fun Zone!

It is time to write a monster story!

Continue this monster story on a separate piece of paper.

That is a good story! You can now find and colour **Shape 3** on the Monster Match page!

I did not tell my Dad about the orange monster I found under my bed because…

What happens next?

Word Beginnings

Gran is going to the wild wood
to look for mini-monsters.
She has asked Tizz to go with her.
Tizz wants to **br**ing her camera
on the **tr**ip.

Words can start with these beginnings:

c-r, b-r, t-r, p-r, d-r, g-r.

Say each individual sound in the word.
Then blend them together.

b-r-i-ng = **br**ing

t-r-i-p = **tr**ip

c-r-u-s-t = **cr**ust

1 Blend these sounds together to make words.
The first one has been done for you.

a b→r→i→ng = <u>bring</u>

b→r→i→ck = _____

b→r→a→g = _____

b d→r→a→g = _____

d→r→o→p = _____

d→r→i→p = _____

c p→r→a→m = _____

p→r→o→d = _____

p→r→o→p = _____

d c→r→a→ck = _____

c→r→u→s→t = _____

c→r→o→p = _____

e g→r→a→b = _____

g→r→i→p = _____

g→r→u→ff = _____

f t→r→a→p = _____

t→r→u→ck = _____

t→r→i→p = _____

2 Choose the correct letters to begin each word.
The first one has been done for you.

a f-r · d-r

dr um

b g-r · p-r

_____ass

c t-r · p-r

_____am

d t-r · b-r

_____uck

3 Choose one of the words from **2** to complete each sentence.

a You drive a _____.

b A baby goes in a _____.

c You bang a _____.

d A cow eats _____.

Fun Zone!

Time to make a scary spider!

Scary! You can now find and colour **Shape 4** on the Monster Match page!

Scary Spiders

You will need black card, scissors, glue and white crayons (or chalk).

Ask an adult to help when needed.

1 Cut an oval and a circle from the black card for the body and head.
2 Cut four identical long, thin strips of black card for the legs.
3 Glue the round head to the oval body.
4 Glue the legs onto the back of the body to make four legs at each side of the body. Then turn it over.
5 Bend the eight legs in half and again where the legs meet the body.
6 Use white crayons to draw some eyes on your spider's head.

igh Sounds

I go mining in the caves.
Sometimes it is as black as n**igh**t!
I have to use a torch to make
it l**igh**t.

When the letters **igh** come
together, the **three** letters make
the 'i' sound (as in p**ie**).

l→**igh**→t = light

n→**igh**→t = night

Dad needs a l**igh**t to see at n**igh**t.

1 Add the **igh** sound to each of the words.
Write the whole words below.
The first one has been done for you.

a h_igh___
   high

c s_____

e n_____t

b l_____t

d r_____t

f t_____t

2 Write an **igh** word that means the opposite to these words.
Use the words from **1** to help you.
The first one has been done for you.

a low _high_

c left _____

e day _____

b loose _____

d dark _____

3 Underline all the **igh** words in this story.
The first one has been done for you.

The princess gave a deep <u>sigh</u>. She had been locked up in a high tower by a wicked queen. She was frightened. There was not much light at night. Just then there was a sound right outside. The princess looked out. What a sight met her eyes! A handsome prince was there on a white horse. He threw up a rope with all his might. The princess held on tight as she climbed down. She was free at last.

4 Make a list of the **igh** words you found in the story.

_____

_____

_____

_____

Fun Zone!

Join the dots in the correct number order to make the picture.

Well done! You can now find and colour **Shape 5** on the Monster Match page!

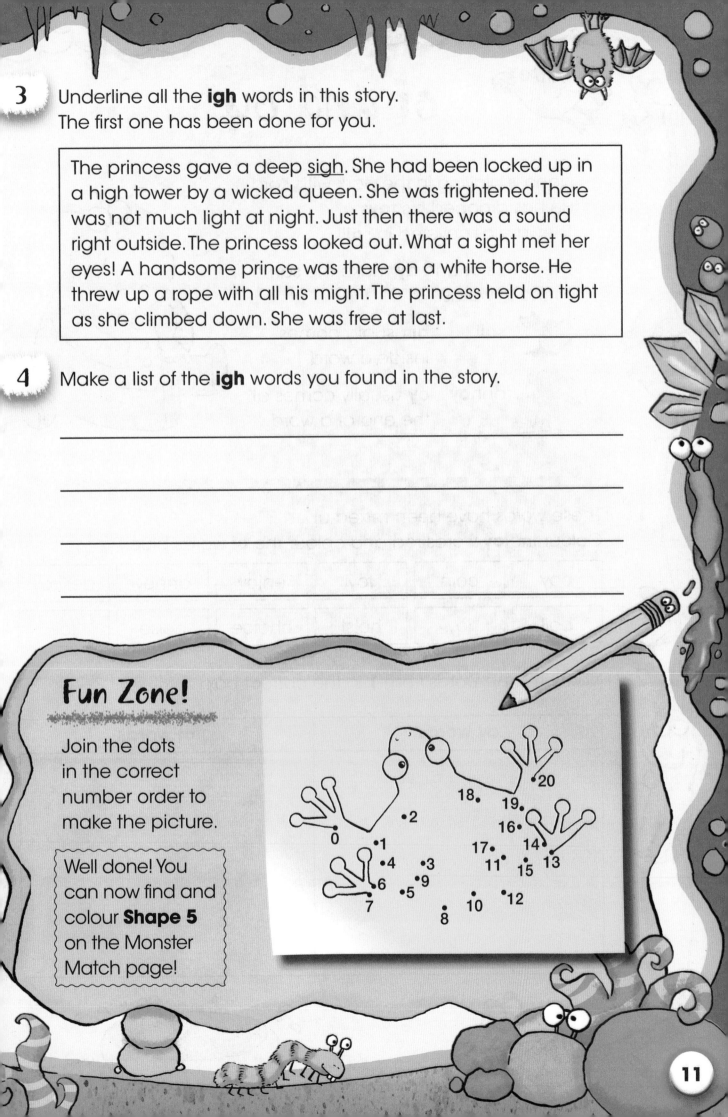

oi and oy

Nano is playing in the park with Kora.
He has dropped his t**oy**s.
They are all covered in s**oi**l!

The letters **oi** and **oy** make the same sound in words.

s**oi**l   **oi** usually comes inside a word.

ann**oy**   **oy** usually comes at the end of a word.

1 These words have been mixed up.
Colour the **oy** words red and colour the **oi** words blue.

boy	coin	toy	enjoy	annoy	destroy
boil	joy	hoist	choice	noise	foil

2 Now write the words from **1** in the correct box.

oy words	oi words

3 Choose and write the correct word under each picture.

| coin   toy   point   destroy |

a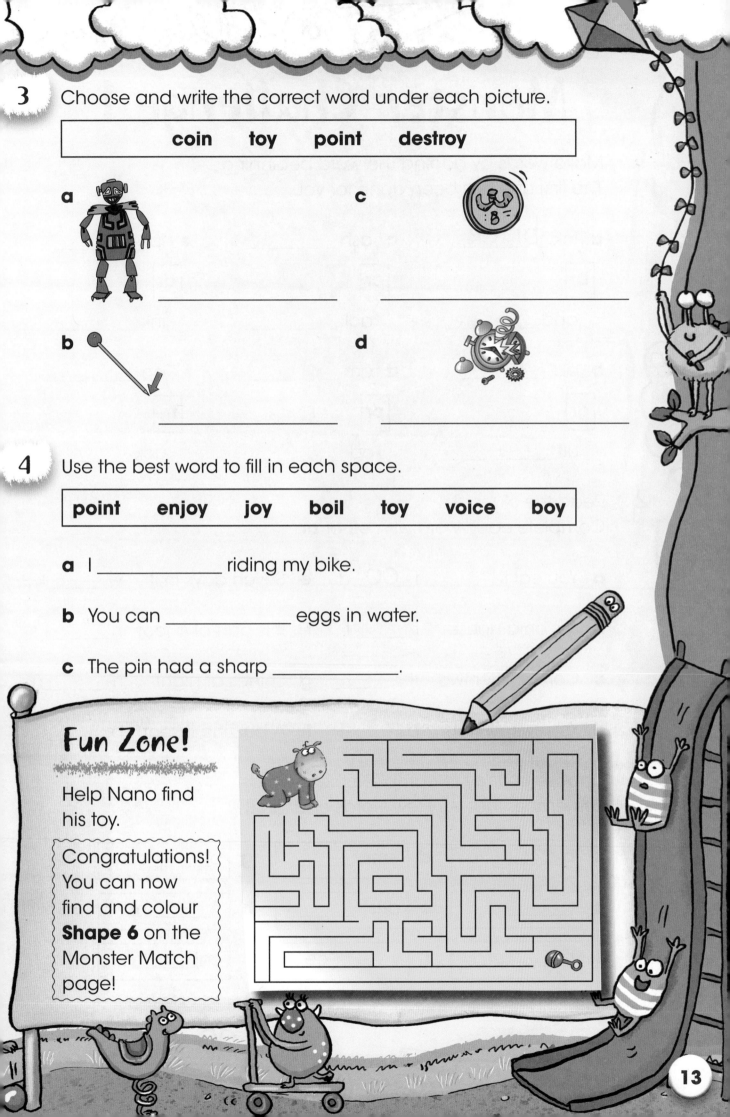

_____

c

_____

b

_____

d

_____

4 Use the best word to fill in each space.

| point   enjoy   joy   boil   toy   voice   boy |

a I _____ riding my bike.

b You can _____ eggs in water.

c The pin had a sharp _____.

Fun Zone!

Help Nano find his toy.

Congratulations! You can now find and colour **Shape 6** on the Monster Match page!

Monster Challenge 1

1 Make words by adding the word beginnings.
The first one has been done for you.

a ick <u>brick</u>

br

   and _____

c ash _____

cr

   ack _____

e ip _____

dr

   ink _____

b ab _____

gr

   uff _____

d am _____

pr

   od _____

f ap _____

tr

   uck _____

2 Read the clues.
Complete each word with **ee** or **oo**.

a You eat it   f_<u>oo</u>_d   **e** Seven days in it   w_____k

b It is on a house   r_____f   **f** It is part of a foot h_____l

c Comes after two   thr_____   **g** Shines at night   m_____n

d You swim in this   p_____l   **h** A buzzing insect   b_____

3 Choose **oi** or **oy** to complete these words.
Remember that very few words end in **oi**!

a b_____

d empl_____

g p_____son

b t_____

e destr_____

h p_____nt

c t_____let

f v_____ce

i enj_____

4 Tick ✓ the real words.
Cross ✗ the nonsense words.

a toy ☐ **d** boy ☐ **g** coin ☐

b doyd ☐ **e** moyd ☐ **h** join ☐

c voisk ☐ **f** enjoy ☐ **i** boin ☐

5 Underline the 'hidden' **igh** words.
Write each word you find.
The first one has been done for you.

a qwe<u>high</u>r ___high___   **f** uiopsighas _____

b dfgthighjk _____   **g** bsightbnmv _____

c tightmnbvc_____   **h** arightdfgh _____

d zxcmightvb_____   **i** nmfightkjh _____

e xlightaqwr _____   **j** asdfgbright _____

6 Put the real words and nonsense words in the correct boxes.
One has been done for you.

high   kigh   right   quigh   bright   vigh   knight   zigh

Real words	Nonsense words
	kigh

15

Long Vowel Sounds

Kora is having a birthday party.
There will be **ca**k**e** on a **pla**t**e**.
Mak**e** sure you are not **la**t**e**!

Long vowel sounds	Words
ai, ay, a-e	sn**ai**l, d**ay**, c**a**k**e**
ee, ea, y, e-e	s**ee**, p**ea**, reall**y**, th**e**s**e**
ie, igh, y, i-e	p**ie**, s**igh**, sh**y**, f**i**v**e**
oe, oa, ow, o-e	t**oe**, b**oa**t, sn**ow**, h**o**m**e**
ue, oo, ew, u-e	cl**ue**, f**oo**d, ch**ew**, t**u**n**e**

You can see that some long vowel sounds
are split.

1 Write the words below.
The first one has been done for you.

a s+**a**+m+**e** = __same__   **d** r+**o**+b+**e** = _____

b c+**a**+n+**e** = _____   **e** r+**i**+d+**e** = _____

c p+**i**+p+**e** = _____   **f** c+**u**+t+**e** = _____

2 Write the long vowel sound **a-e**, **i-e** or **o-e** next to each word.
The first has been done for you.

a t**a**p**e** = __a-e__   **d** m**a**t**e** = _____

b c**a**p**e** = _____   **e** m**o**p**e** = _____

c p**i**n**e** = _____   **f** sh**i**n**e** = _____

3 Choose and write the correct word for each picture.

a hat/hate

_____

c mop/mope

_____

b rid/ride

_____

d tub/tube

_____

4 Write each sentence again.
Correct the underlined word.
The first one has been done for you.

a I <u>cane</u> ride my bike.

I can ride my bike.

c I can <u>wine</u> the race.

_____

b I drink water from the <u>tape</u>.

_____

d I <u>hop</u> you get well soon.

_____

Fun Zone!

Some monsters are having a tea party! Think of all the things they would have.

A marvellous monster tea party! You can now find and colour **Shape 7** on the Monster Match page!

On a separate piece of paper, think about what monsters would have at a party.

• What would they eat?
  Perhaps they would eat mud pies and slime sandwiches?

• What would they drink?
  What about a glass of beetle juice?

• Would they have party games?
  They could play 'pin the tail on the monster'!

air, ear and are Sounds

Gran was searching for mini-monsters.
She came across a b**ear**!
He was big and brown and
had lots of h**air**.
He gave her quite a sc**are**!

The groups of letters **air** and **ear** can
make the same sounds in words.
We just have to learn when to use them.

b→**ear** = b**ear**   p→**air** = p**air**

Sometimes words with **are** sound the
same as **ear** and **air** words too.

c→**are** = c**are**   sh→**are** = sh**are**

1 Write the words below.
The first one has been done for you.

a p→air = _pair_   **d** w→ear = _____   **g** c→are = _____

b h→air = _____   **e** b→ear = _____   **h** d→are = _____

c ch→air = _____   **f** p→ear = _____   **i** s→c→are = _____

2 Put the words from **1** into the correct boxes.

air words	**ear** words	**are** words

3 Write the correct word for each picture.

a

c

_____ _____

b

d

_____ _____

4 Match these words to their meaning.

chair   **pear**   **bear**   **hair**

a A huge and hairy animal _____

b A fruit _____

c It grows on your head _____

d Something you sit on _____

Fun Zone!

Now you can make a bear of your own!

Well done! You can now find **Shape 8** on the Monster Match page and colour it in!

Bear Face

You will need a paper plate, brown paper, crayons, scissors and glue.

Ask an adult to help when needed.

1 Cut out three circles from the brown paper.
2 Glue one circle in the middle of the paper plate and the other two to the top of the paper plate for ears.
3 Use crayons to draw some eyes, a nose and a mouth for your bear's face.

-s and -es Endings

Webber is looking after Nano.
Nano has so many toy**s**.
He throws them all around the room!
Webber has four arm**s** so he catch**es** them all.

To make **nouns** (words for people, places or things) plural, you can **add -s** to the endings.

singular	plural – just add s
 one dog	two dog**s**

If a **verb** (a doing or being words) ends with **ss**, **zz**, **x**, **ch**, or **sh**, you just add **-es**.

ru**sh** = ru**shes**   hi**ss** = hi**sses**
I ru**sh**   He ru**shes**   I hi**ss**   It hi**sses**

1 Write the new words.
The first one has been done for you.

a cat+s = __cats__   d tube+s = _____

b rock+s = _____   e arm+s = _____

c toy+s = _____   f coin+s = _____

2 Write the new words you make.
The first one has been done for you.

a catch+es = __catches__   d push+es = _____

b wash+es = _____   e match+es = _____

c touch+es = _____   f watch+es = _____

3 Draw a line to join the words with their correct endings.
Write the new words you make.
The first one has been done for you.

a cat ――― es   _____

b wish ―――― s   cats

c dog   es   _____

d push   s   _____

4 Write each sentence and add **s** or **es** to the underlined words.
Remember to check if the word ends in ss, zz, x, ch or sh.
The first one has been done for you.

a Dad saved the <u>cat</u>.

   Dad saved the cats.

b Nano <u>play</u> with his toys.

_____

c Grandpa <u>fix</u> things.

_____

d Gran <u>watch</u> wildlife.

_____

Fun Zone!

Complete this crossword. All of the answers are on these two pages.

Congratulations! You can now find and colour **Shape 9** on the Monster Match page!

Across
5 Who fixes things?
6 What does Nano like to play with?

Down
1 How many arms does Webber have?
2 What do we call pieces of money made of metal?
3 What did Dad save?
4 What does a snake do?

un- Beginnings

Poggo and Litmus are playing a ball game.
Poggo wins and is very happy!
Litmus was very **un**lucky.
Now he is **un**happy.

Adding **un**– to the beginning of words makes them have opposite meanings.

un+happy = **un**happy

This means that you are **not** happy.

1 Underline **un**- in the words below.
The first one has been done for you.

a <u>un</u>happy

b undo

c unlock

d unload

e unzip

f unpack

2 Write the opposite of the words below.
The first one has been done for you.

a unhappy _happy_

b undo _____

c unlock _____

d unload _____

e unzip _____

f unpack _____

3 Write the new words.
The first one has been done for you.

a un+zip = _unzip_ **d** un+fold = _____

b un+seen = _____ **e** un+tie = _____

c un+dress = _____ **f** un+lucky = _____

4 Choose the correct word to complete each sentence.

unzip	unpack	unhappy	untie

a Litmus had to _____ his shoelaces.

b Tizz had to _____ her new camera case.

c Dad had to _____ his suitcase.

d Fizz was _____ about leaving Tizz.

Fun Zone!

It is time to make some happy and unhappy monster faces.

They are both great! You can now find and colour **Shape 10** on the Monster Match page!

Monster Faces

You will need two paper plates, glue, crayons and decorations.

Ask an adult to help when needed.

1 On one paper plate, draw a happy face with crayons.
2 Glue your decorations onto the face to make it a happy monster face.
3 On the other paper plate, use crayons to draw an unhappy face.
4 Add decorations to the face using glue to make your unhappy monster face.

-ing and -ed Endings

Tizz and Fizz play**ed** in the park with Nano.
Tizz and Fizz jump**ed** in the muddy puddles.
Nano is too young to jump in the muddy puddles.
He likes play**ing** in the mud though!

Verbs (doing or being words) can be written in the past or present tense.
You can add -**ed** or -**ing** to the end of words.

Root word	Past tense	Present tense
jump	jump**ed**	jump**ing**

1 Write the new words.
The first one has been done for you.

a jump+ed = __jumped__   **d** buzz+ed = _____

b rain+ed = _____   **e** crash+ed = _____

c hunt+ed = _____   **f** miss+ed = _____

2 Try these words.
The first one has been done for you.

a wear+ing = __wearing__   **d** play+ing = _____

b enjoy+ing = _____   **e** lift+ing = _____

c melt+ing = _____   **f** splash+ing = _____

3 Complete these words by adding -**ing** and -**ed**.
The first one has been done for you.

a rain _ing_   rain _ed_

b play _____   play _____

c walk _____   walk _____

d cook _____   cook _____

4 Choose the correct word to complete each sentence.
The first one has been done for you.

a Tizz (walked, walking) _walked_ to school.

b Litmus (missed, missing) _____ his friend Poggo.

c Zak (playing, played) _____ with his frisbee.

d Poggo (enjoying, enjoyed) _____ listening to music.

Fun Zone!

Time to make a paper bag monster!

Brilliant! You can now find and colour **Shape 11** on the Monster Match page!

Paper Bag Monster

You will need a paper bag, coloured paint, coloured paper, glue, scissors, tape and newspaper.

Ask an adult to help when needed.

1 With the paper bag lying flat, use paint to decorate.
2 Cut out some eyes, hair and a mouth from the coloured paper and glue them onto the paper bag.
3 Crumple some old newspaper and fill the paper bag.
4 Tape the end of the paper bag closed.

-er and -est

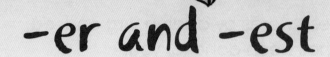

The Professor wants to find out who is the tall**est** monster in the class.
Fizz, Tizz and Kora all line up in order of height.
Tizz is tall**er** than Fizz but Kora is the tall**est**.

-er and **-est** can be added to adjectives (describing words).
These endings mean that you can compare things.

Adjective	add -er	add -est
tall	tall**er**	tall**est**

1 Write the new words.
The first one has been done for you.

a quick+er = _quicker_   **c** tall+er = _____

b cold+er = _____   **d** fresh+er = _____

Poggo is tall**er** than Nano.

2 Write the new words.
The first one has been done for you.

a quick+est = _quickest_   **c** tall+est = _____

b cold+est = _____   **d** fresh+est = _____

Out of all the monsters, the Professor is the tall**est**!

3 Complete this table by adding -**er** and -**est**.

Adjective	Add -er	Add -est
quick	quicker	quickest
warm		
fast		
fresh		
short		

4 Complete the sentences below by adding -**er** to the words in brackets.
The first one has been done for you.

a Leckie is (tall) _____taller_____ than Zak.

b Nano is (short) _____ than Poggo.

c Tizz is (slow) _____ than Fizz.

d Dad is (old) _____ than Mum.

Fun Zone!

Answer these monster questions.

Well done! You can now find and colour **Shape 12** on the Monster Match page!

Monster Facts

Which of your friends is the tallest?
_____

Which of your friends is the shortest?
_____

Who is the oldest person in your family?
_____

Who is the youngest person in your family?
_____

Can you think of some more questions?
Ask a friend!

Monster Challenge 2

1 Sort the words in the box into two sets.
The first one has been done for you.

five	like	came	time	safe
made	same	side	ride	take

a-e words	i-e words
made	

2 Choose and write the correct word to match the picture.

a 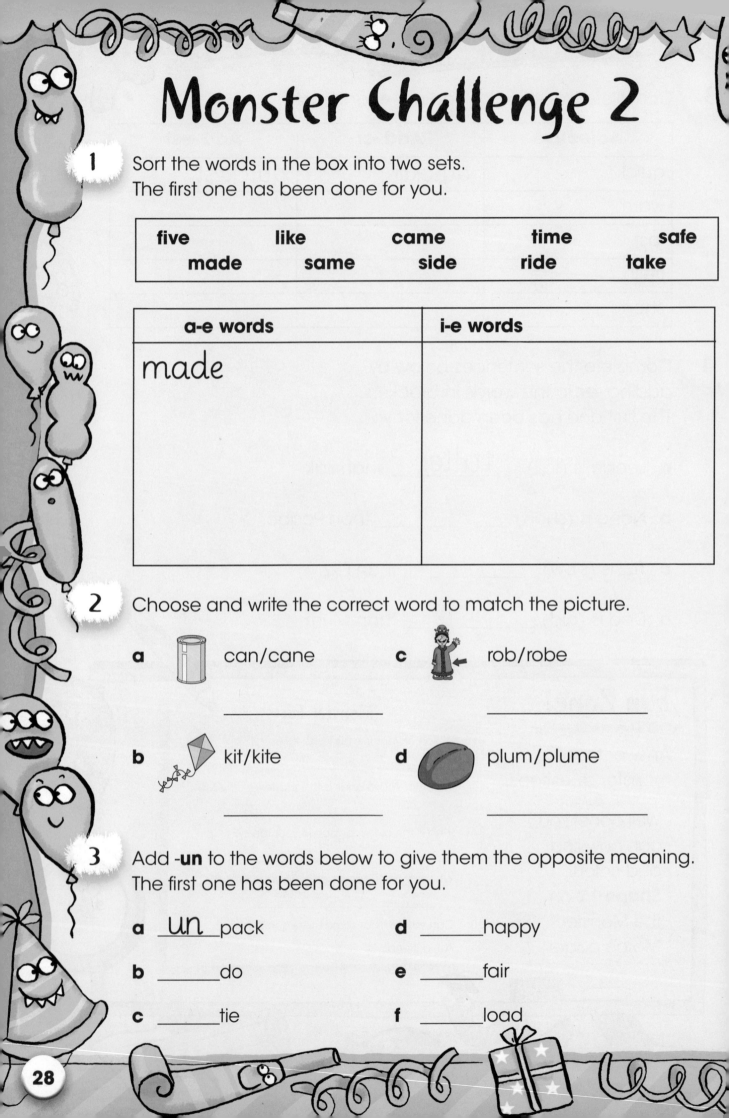 can/cane

_____

c rob/robe

_____

b kit/kite

_____

d plum/plume

_____

3 Add **-un** to the words below to give them the opposite meaning.
The first one has been done for you.

a _un_pack

d _____happy

b _____do

e _____fair

c _____tie

f _____load

28

4 Add **-s** or **-es** to these words.
The first one has been done for you.

a dog _____dogs_____

d rock _____

b cat _____

e catch _____

c boat _____

f match_____

5 Add **-ed** to these words.
The first one has been done for you.

a jump __jumped__

d rush _____

b hunt _____

e open _____

c push _____

f buzz _____

6 Complete the sentences below by adding **-est** to the words in brackets.
The first one has been done for you.

a Mum has the (clean) ___cleanest___ home in Monsterville.

b The Professor has the (fast) _____ car on the road.

c Poggo is the (quick) _____ monster.

I knew you could do it!

You have made it to the end of the book.

You are a magnificent monster!

Answers

Page 2
1 a, e, i, m, o, t, u, w, y

Page 3
2

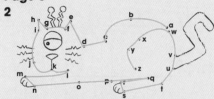

Fun zone

j	u	m	p	s	e	r	o
l	v	y	v	q	f	v	v
a	i	y	g	u	o	q	e
z	z	i	p	i	x	s	r
y	o	o	m	c	r	t	o
t	d	o	g	k	d	s	u
h	b	b	r	o	w	n	c
e	w	y	u	u	f	r	p

Page 4
1 **a** hat **c** peg **e** pen **g** dig **i** mud
b rod **d** tub **f** wig **h** pan

Page 5
2 jam—fan, bed—leg, log—dot, bib—zip, cub—pup
3 **a** zip **c** log **e** bed **g** dot **i** pup
b jam **d** cub **f** leg **h** bib **j** fan

Fun zone

Page 6
1 **a** peel **b** see **c** tree **d** green **e** meet
2 **a** pool **b** food **c** moon **d** soon **e** zoo

Page 7
3 **a** seed weed **b** hoop loop **c** keep deep **d** hoof roof **e** week peek **f** room zoom
4 **a** week **c** free **e** root **g** noon **i** need
b troop **d** weep **f** green **h** mood **j** heel

Page 8
1 **a** bring, brick, brag
b drag, drop, drip
c pram, prod, prop
d crack, crust, crop
e grab, grip, gruff
f trap, truck, trip

Page 9
2 **a** drum **b** grass **c** pram **d** truck
3 **a** truck **b** pram **c** drum **d** grass

Page 10
1 **a** high **b** light **c** sigh **d** right **e** night **f** tight
2 **a** high **b** tight **c** right **d** light **e** night

Page 11
3 and 4 sigh, high, frightened, light, night, right, sight, might, tight

Fun zone

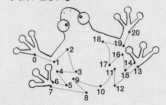

Page 12
1 and 2 oy words (red): boy, joy, toy, enjoy, annoy, destroy
oi words (blue): boil, coin, hoist, choice, noise, foil

Page 13
3 **a** toy **b** point **c** coin **d** destroy
4 **a** enjoy **b** boil **c** point

Fun zone

Page 14
1 **a** brick, brand **c** crash, crack **e** drip, drink
b grab, gruff **d** pram, prod **f** trap, truck
2 **a** food **c** three **e** week **g** moon
b roof **d** pool **f** heel **h** bee
3 **a** boy **c** toilet **e** destroy **g** poison **i** enjoy
b toy **d** employ **f** voice **h** point

Page 15

4 **a** toy✓   **c** voisk✗   **e** moyd✗   **g** coin✓   **i** boin✗
   b doyd✗   **d** boy✓   **f** enjoy✓   **h** join✓

5 **a** high   **c** tight   **e** light **g** sight   **i** fight
   (or sigh)

   b thigh   **d** might   **f** sigh   **h** right   **j** bright
   (or high)

6 **Real words:** high, right, bright, knight
   Nonsense words: kigh, quigh, vigh, zigh

Page 16

1 **a** same **b** cane **c** pipe **d** robe **e** ride **f** cute
2 **a** a-e **b** a-e **c** i-e **d** a-e **e** o-e **f** i-e

Page 17

3 **a** hat **b** ride **c** mop **d** tube
4 **a** I can ride my bike.
   b I drink water from the tap.
   c I can win the race.
   d I hope you get well soon.

Page 18

1 **a** pair   **c** chair   **e** bear   **g** care   **i** scare
   b hair   **d** wear   **f** pear   **h** dare

2 **air words:** pair, hair, chair, **ear words:** wear,
   bear, pear, **are words:** care, dare, scare

Page 19

3 **a** chair **b** hair **c** pear **d** bear
4 **a** bear **b** pear **c** hair **d** chair

Page 20

1 **a** cats   **c** toys   **e** arms
   b rocks   **d** tubes   **f** coins
2 **a** catches   **c** touches   **e** matches
   b washes   **d** pushes   **f** watches

Page 21

3 **a** cats **b** wishes **c** dogs **d** pushes
4 **a** Dad saved the cats.
   b Nano plays with his toys.
   c Grandpa fixes things.
   d Gran watches wildlife.

Fun zone

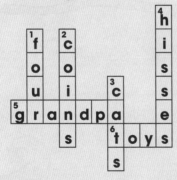

Page 22

1 **a** unhappy **c** unlock **e** unzip
   b undo   **d** unload **f** unpack
2 **a** happy **b** do **c** lock **d** load **e** zip **f** pack

Page 23

3 **a** unzip   **c** undress   **e** untie
   b unseen **d** unfold   **f** unlucky
4 **a** untie   **c** unpack (or unzip)
   b unzip (or unpack) **d** unhappy

Page 24

1 **a** jumped   **c** hunted   **e** crashed
   b rained   **d** buzzed   **f** missed
2 **a** wearing   **c** melting   **e** lifting
   b enjoying   **d** playing   **f** splashing

Page 25

3 **a** raining, rained   **c** walking, walked
   b playing, played   **d** cooking, cooked
4 **a** Tizz walked to school.
   b Litmus missed his friend Poggo.
   c Zak played with his frisbee.
   d Poggo enjoyed listening to the music.

Page 26

1 **a** quicker **b** colder **c** taller **d** fresher
2 **a** quickest **b** coldest **c** tallest **d** freshest

Page 27

3

Adjective	Add -er	Add -est
quick	quicker	quickest
warm	warmer	warmest
fast	faster	fastest
fresh	fresher	freshest
short	shorter	shortest

4 **a** Leckie is taller than Zak.
   b Nano is shorter than Poggo.
   c Tizz is slower than Fizz.
   d Dad is older than Mum.

Page 28

1 **a-e words:** made, came, safe, same, take
   i-e words: five, like, time, side, ride
2 **a** can **b** kite **c** robe **d** plum
3 **a** unpack   **c** untie   **e** unfair
   b undo   **d** unhappy **f** unload

Page 29

4 **a** dogs   **c** boats **e** catches
   b cats   **d** rocks **f** matches
5 **a** jumped   **c** pushed   **e** opened
   b hunted   **d** rushed   **f** buzzed
6 **a** Mum has the cleanest home in Monsterville.
   b The Professor has the fastest car on
   the road.
   c Poggo is the quickest monster.

Monster Match

Each time you complete a topic in this book, you will be awarded a shape number.

Find and colour the shapes in the picture of Nano that match the numbers you have been given.

As you work through the book you will gradually see Nano come to life!